SCHOLASTIC
Phonics

Tam In a Pit

Can you spot the cat on 4 pages?

Published in the UK by Scholastic Education, 2021
Book End, Range Road, Witney, Oxfordshire, OX29 0YD
Scholastic Ireland, 89E Lagan Road, Dublin Industrial Estate, Glasnevin, Dublin, D11 HP5F

SCHOLASTIC and associated logos are trademarks and/or registered trademarks of Scholastic Inc.
www.scholastic.co.uk
© 2021 Scholastic Limited
1 2 3 4 5 6 7 8 9 1 2 3 4 5 6 7 8 9 0

Printed by Ashford Colour Press
Paper made from wood grown in sustainable forests and other controlled sources.

A CIP catalogue record for this book is available from the British Library.

ISBN 978-0702-30860-4

Author
Catherine Baker
Editorial team
Rachel Morgan, Tracy Kewley, Liz Evans
Design team
Dipa Mistry, We Are Grace
Illustrations
Kevin Payne

It is a din.

Tam is sad.

tip

4

pat
pat

7

Retell the story